LifeTimes

The Story of Anne Frank

by Stewart Ross
illustrated by Alan Marks

Belitha Press

First published in the UK in 2001 by

 Belitha Press Ltd
    London House, Great London Wharf
    Parkgate Road, London SW11 4NQ

Produced for Belitha Press by

W White-Thomson Publishing Ltd
    2/3 St Andrew's Place
    Lewes, BN7 1UP

For Tom Dash, Alys Barr and their teacher, Ian Witts (SR)

ISBN 1 84138 340 6

British Library Cataloguing in Publication Data for this book is
available from the British Library.

Editor: Steve White-Thomson
Designer: Simon Borrough
Language consultant: Norah Granger, Senior Lecturer in Primary
    Education at the University of Brighton.

With thanks to Kay Barnham for her editorial help in the latter
stages of this book.

Printed in China

Introduction

It was the middle of May, 1940. The Second World War was raging in Europe. The Nazis had taken over Germany and attacked the countries around them. During the last few days they had defeated the Dutch.

In the Dutch city of Amsterdam a father and daughter were watching the enemy arrive…

The Lorries

The noise went on and on. Anne Frank let go of her father's hand and covered her ears. She stood back from the edge of the pavement and stared at the roaring stream of dark lorries. They were all full of soldiers.

When the last lorry had gone round the corner, Anne lowered her hands. She looked up at her father. He was a tall, handsome man dressed in a neat, grey suit and brown hat.

'Is that the end of the war, Daddy?' she asked, feeling for his hand again.

Mr Frank looked down at his ten-year-old daughter and smiled gently. Anne knew the look well. It said, 'I am smiling because I love you, not because I am happy.' He lifted his eyes and looked at where the lorries had been. 'It is the end of the war for the Dutch. But it is not the end of the war for us.'

Anne frowned. She didn't understand.

'Those soldiers were Nazis,' her father went on. 'They are in charge of the city now.'

'But I don't understand what you mean,' said Anne. 'Why isn't it the end of the war for us?'

Mr Frank checked to see that no one was listening. 'Anne, we are Jews,' he said in a low voice. 'The Nazis hate all Jews.'

'Then I hate all Nazis!' said Anne crossly.

Before she could say anything else, her father put his hand over her mouth.

'Never say that again!' he ordered.

Anne was shocked. Her father was normally such a gentle man. Why was he acting like this? She felt hot tears come into her eyes.

Mr Frank took away his hand.

'I'm sorry, Anne,' he said, bending down and putting his arm round her. 'But you must be very careful what you say now. Just in case. Promise me?'

Anne quickly wiped her eyes on her sleeve. 'Yes. I promise.' When she looked up at her father's face, she saw something she had never seen before. He was afraid.

The Frank family were German Jews. The leader of the Nazis, Adolf Hitler, blamed the Jews for everything that went wrong in Germany. So when the Nazis took over Germany in 1933, the Franks moved to Holland to get away from them.

The Nazis treated the Jews very badly. Now the Nazis had invaded Holland, the Frank family and other Jews who lived there were in real danger.

The Cloud

There was a strange silence in the flat when
Anne and her father arrived home.

Mr Frank sat down at once and pretended
to read the paper. Anne's mother, Edith, was
preparing tea in the kitchen. Grandma was
knitting. Anne's older sister, Margot, sat
tucked up on the sofa. When Anne tried
to talk to her, she told her to go away.

Only the cat, Moortie, was still friendly.
Anne picked her up and cuddled her.

'What's the matter, Moortie?' she asked.
'Is it the Nazis?' The cat stared at Anne with
deep green eyes and licked her hand.

'Dear Moortie!' Anne smiled.
'Everything will be OK, won't it?'

Moortie carried on licking.

The next day everyone was more cheerful.
At school, Anne's friends talked about the
lorries and the soldiers, but they were not
worried. By the time of her eleventh birthday,
on 12 June, Anne had almost forgotten about
the Nazis. They were like a cloud that had
blotted out the sun for a while and then
blown away again.

By the spring, the cloud had returned.

One Saturday morning, Jan, Mary and some
of Anne's other classmates were talking about
going to the cinema. Anne rather liked Jan,
a tall boy with a mop of straight fair hair.

'Great!' she cried. 'Can I come?'

Mary stared at her.

'You? Of course not, Anne. Don't be silly.'
Anne felt her bottom lip trembling.

'Why not? I'm your friend, aren't I?'

'Of course you are,' said Jan. 'But you're a Jew, aren't you? Jews aren't allowed to go to the cinema any more. Nazi orders.'

Anne felt like crying and shouting and screaming all at the same time. She wanted to say how much she hated the Nazis and their stupid laws. But then she remembered the promise she'd made to her father.

With an effort, she looked Jan in the eye.

'Of course,' she said slowly. 'I don't want you to get into trouble for being with a Jew. Go to the cinema without me. Anyway, I'm busy on Saturday,' she added, trying to hide her disappointment.

The Nazi cloud grew thicker and darker. One morning that summer, Mrs Frank came into Anne's room and sat on the edge of her bed. 'I've news for you, Anne darling,' she said. When she reached for her daughter's hand, Anne knew that the news was bad.

'Next term you and Margot will be starting a new school,' said Mrs Frank quietly.

Anne's face fell. 'But I don't want—'

'It's not a question of what you want, Anne,' interrupted her mother. 'It's the law. Jews are not allowed to go to school with Dutch children any more.'

Life for the Jews in Germany was terrible by 1941. Most were rounded up and sent to concentration camps.

The Nazis and their Dutch supporters began treating the Dutch Jews in the same way. They were banned from public places such as cinemas, restaurants and swimming pools. Later, Jews and non-Jews were not allowed to work together.

The Lucky One

Anne quickly settled into the Jewish Secondary School. One of her best friends, Hanneli Goslar, also went there. The teachers liked Anne, and so did the other pupils. Peter Wessel, a lad with a mischievous gleam in his eye, enjoyed cycling home with her through the cobbled streets. He said the way her glossy black hair blew out behind her reminded him of a wild pony.

The winter of 1941–2 was long and hard.
Because of the war, food was scarce and there
was a lot of illness.

Shortly after Christmas Anne's grandma caught a chill. Within a week she was dead.

Anne had loved her grandma dearly – almost as much as her mother and father. Now, she felt as if a piece of her heart had broken off. Something her parents said upset her, too.

After the funeral, Anne heard her father say, 'It's sad, Edith. But she may be the lucky one.'

'I'm afraid you're right, Otto,' Mrs Frank sighed. 'In some ways I envy her.'

Only later, when terrible things were happening, did Anne realize what her parents had meant.

Meanwhile, the laws against the Jews were
becoming stricter and stricter. So everyone
could recognize them, Jews had to wear a
yellow Star of David sewn on to their clothes.
And they were not allowed out after eight
o'clock at night.

One evening Anne went for a walk with
her new boyfriend, Harry Goldberg.

When they arrived home ten minutes late, Mr Frank was waiting on the doorstep. He was seething with anger.

'You silly girl!' he hissed. 'Didn't you think of the danger?'

Anne was confused. Then she noticed that her father's eyes were fixed on something across the road. She turned to see a pair of soldiers standing in the shadows. They were watching her closely.

Life for the Jews of Amsterdam had become even worse by May 1942. They were not allowed to drive, use public transport or even own a bike. They could shop for only two hours a day, and only in shops with the sign 'Jewish Shop'.

Terrible news came from Germany. The Nazis had started to kill the Jews in the concentration camps with poison gas.

Dear Kitty…

The summer started brilliantly.

Anne had a really good report from school. She managed to spend lots of time with Harry, playing table-tennis and going to one of the ice-cream shops that were still open to Jews.

Best of all, for her thirteenth birthday her parents gave her a diary.

Anne loved writing. The diary, which she called Kitty, was soon her best friend – better even than Hanneli or Moortie. Whenever she had a quiet moment, she took up her pen and began, 'Dear Kitty...'

Only Kitty knew Anne's secret hopes and fears. Her biggest fear was what the Nazis would do next.

Mr Frank shared his daughter's fear. One afternoon, when he was out walking with Anne and Margot, he suddenly turned to them and said, 'You know we'll have to go into hiding soon, don't you?'

Anne looked at him in amazement.

'Hiding?' she asked. 'Why on earth should we go into hiding, Daddy?'

'Because,' he replied, 'it's better to disappear before the Nazis come looking for us.' He put an arm round her shoulder. 'We should go before it's too late.'

Anne nodded. 'But when will we hide?' she asked. 'And where?'

'Don't worry,' her father replied. 'Just enjoy yourself for the moment. You'll know when the time comes.'

The time came sooner than Anne expected.
Three days later, when she was reading a book
on the balcony, the front door bell rang.
Margot went to answer it.

Shortly afterwards, she came rushing back
upstairs. 'It was Nazis,' she panted. 'They want
Daddy. They're sending him to a work camp.'

Although it was a hot July afternoon, Anne
shivered. She knew what work camp meant.
It meant a long journey to the east, starvation
and almost certain death. She couldn't believe
it. Not her own father…

She passed the rest of the afternoon in a
daze. Several of the family's Dutch friends
came and went. Early that evening, Margot
joined Anne in their room. The older girl's face
was chalk white and her hands were shaking,
just like Grandma's had done.

'Dearest Anne,' she began, 'I have
something to tell you.' She spoke
automatically, like a machine they
had heard long ago at a fair.
'I made a mistake. The
Nazis were not asking
for Daddy. They were
asking for me. They
want *me* to go to
a work camp!'

Anne threw her arms round Margot's neck. 'No!' she cried. 'Not you! Not anyone! You're only 16. They can't take you away!'

Margot took out a handkerchief and dabbed her sister's eyes.

'No, of course they can't. Mummy promised. Come on, Anne, we need to get packed. We're going into hiding. Now.'

Now, Jews were not allowed to own or run businesses. The Nazis took over the businesses and gave them to others. Otto Frank had expected this to happen. He had already handed over his business to two Dutch friends, Victor Kugler and Johannes Kleiman, who were running it for him.

Into Hiding

Mrs Frank woke Anne at dawn. She explained
to her daughter that they could not take any
luggage with them. The police would know that
a Jew carrying a suitcase was trying to escape.
Anne could take only her school satchel and
the clothes she was wearing.

Anne had already crammed her satchel full
of her favourite possessions, including Kitty.
She now dressed as if she were going to the
North Pole – two pairs of stockings, two vests,
three pairs of knickers, a dress, a skirt, a jacket,
a coat, shoes, a woolly cap
and a scarf.

Feeling like a giant bear, Anne went to
the window and looked out. Thank goodness!
The hot weather had ended and thin drizzle
was falling from a grey sky.

At half-past seven, Anne said goodbye
to Moortie and followed her parents out into
the wet street. Although she had no idea where
they were going, she didn't mind. She knew
they would be safe.

At the moment, that was all that mattered.

The family made their way through
the city to the building where
Mr Frank worked. Making sure
no one was watching, they
slipped inside and went
upstairs to the office.

They climbed another flight of stairs, turned right and – to Anne's amazement – they were suddenly inside the secret flat that Mr Frank had been preparing for his family.

For a time Anne forgot her fear. It was such an adventure! Once she had unpacked her things and decorated her room with pictures of film stars, she thought that her new home was the most comfortable hiding place in all Holland. What's more, she had something to look forward to.

The Franks were to share their hideaway with the van Pels family. Peter van Pels was 15. Anne couldn't wait to meet him.

The Nazis were now rounding up Jews all over Holland. Many Dutch people risked their lives by helping them to escape or go into hiding.

Several people working in the building knew about the Jews in the secret flat. Victor Kugler and Johannes Kleiman knew. So did Miep and Jan Gies, and Bep Voskuijl and his father.

The Secret World

Through thin curtains the autumn sunshine flooded into the small room. Anne, seated at the table, stared at the numbers in Mr Kugler's book. She had to add up 25 columns, each with 32 numbers in it. What a bore!

But it was thanks to Mr Kugler and his friends that they were still alive. Helping with their book-keeping was the least she could do.

She took a deep breath and started to add
the columns of figures. Five plus 32 equals 37,
plus nine makes…

'Anne, have you brushed your hair this
morning?' It was her mother's voice, nagging.

Anne felt anger rising within her. Still staring
at the figures, she said slowly, 'Mummy, how
many times do I have to tell you that
I'm 13 now? I don't need a nanny.
I'm trying to work.'

'I know that, dear,' replied Mrs Frank.
'But just because we're in hiding, it doesn't
mean we shouldn't take care of ourselves.'

'Hear, hear!' chimed in Mrs van Pels from
the other side of the room.

Anne thought her head would explode.

'Leave me alone!' she muttered through
gritted teeth. 'We've been here more than a
year, and all we do is argue. All day, every day.
I hate it! I hate all of you! I want to run away.'

She slammed down her pencil and stamped into the tiny room she shared with Margot. Throwing herself on to her bed, she buried her face in her hands, sobbing loudly.

Everything had gone wrong. Peter had turned out to be boring. She badly missed her old friends, especially Hanneli. Now she had only Kitty to share her secrets with.

They were all trapped in the secret flat, like chickens in a coop. They got on each other's nerves. They were short of food, soap, clothes, and terrified of the dreaded knock on the door…

Later, her father came talk to her. He spoke softly and kindly. He knew it was difficult, terribly difficult, to live like this. But at least they were alive and safe.

There was hope, too, he explained. In a short time – maybe in the next few months – British and American troops would cross the Channel and drive the Nazis from Holland. They must be patient. They had survived one year, so they could survive another.

Anne put her hand on her father's shoulder. 'Do you believe that, Daddy? Do you really think we will be free soon?'

The seven Jews living in the secret flat were joined on 16 November 1942 by an eighth, Fritz Pfeffer. They all did what they could to help their Dutch protectors. As well as book work, they filled gravy packets and took the stones out of cherries.

We Know Everything!

Autumn dragged into winter, and winter into spring. Still the war raged on. And still the small group of Jews remained shut away from the world.

But now there was real hope. Everywhere, the Nazis were in retreat. The Russians were driving them back in the east and, step by step, they were being forced out of Italy.

Anne was more relaxed, too. As she neared her fifteenth birthday, she was fast becoming a young woman. She was annoyed when others still treated her as a child, but she learned not to react. Besides, she had a new joy in her life.

Over the long months together she had come to see Peter in a different light. There was more to him than she had realized. He was not as clever as her, but he was calmer.

She grew to like him more and more.

Peter was desperately shy. Day by day, sitting with him in the attic where he worked, she encouraged him to talk. And the more he talked, the fonder she became of him. In time, her fondness grew to love. She told Kitty that for the first time in years she felt really happy.

In June came the wonderful news that British and American troops had landed in France. Freedom seemed only weeks away.

On the morning of 4 August, Victor Kugler was disturbed by a loud knocking on his office door. Before he could answer, a group of armed men burst in. The leader wore the unmistakable uniform of a Nazi policeman.

'Don't say a word!' he barked. 'We know everything. Take us to the Jews.' Kugler hesitated. The Nazi raised his pistol. 'Now, Mr Kugler. No trouble, please.'

Kugler led the way to the bookcase that hid the door to the secret flat.

'It's behind there,' he said. Two men pushed the bookcase aside.

At first Anne thought it was a dream. There they all were – her parents, Margot, Mr and Mrs van Pels, Peter and Mr Pfeffer – standing with their backs to the wall, terrified. Had two years of miserable hiding really been in vain?

'Bring me all your valuables,' ordered the policeman in his thick Austrian accent. Then he gave them five minutes to pack. 'Your holiday is over,' he added sarcastically. 'It's time you joined the other Jews and did something useful.'

Clutching her tattered satchel, Anne was hurried down the stairs and pushed towards a waiting lorry. A small crowd had gathered on the street to see what was going on. As Anne passed, an old woman stepped forward and touched her lightly on the arm.

'Good luck, my dear,' she whispered.

Before Anne could reply, she was bundled into the lorry with the others and driven off to prison.

Before the war about 130 000 Jews lived in Holland. The Nazis killed 100 000 of them. They also made thousands of Dutch men and women work in German factories. The city of Amsterdam was not freed until May 1945.

Into the Night

It was now six months since the Franks
had been captured. A bitter wind howled
through the barbed-wire fence of Belsen
concentration camp. Nearby, hundreds
of women prisoners were crammed
into a wooden hut. Sick and
starving, they were stacked
like rubbish sacks in filthy
bunk beds.

The door creaked open. A girl entered and looked about her. Pulling a thin shawl closer around her bony shoulders, she knelt and whispered to one woman, 'Anne Frank? Do you know where I can find Anne Frank?'

The old woman stared at her blankly for a moment. Then she lifted an arm no thicker than a stick and pointed to a far corner. The visitor thanked her and shuffled across the room.

'Hanneli? Hanneli Goslar?' Anne's voice could scarcely be heard above the noise of the wind. 'Is it really you? Why are you here?'

Hanneli forced herself to smile. 'Yes, Anne darling, it's your old friend from Amsterdam. Look, I've brought you something.' She placed a small packet of food on the grimy straw of Anne's mattress.

When her friend stretched out a hand towards it, Hanneli saw that the thin fingers were covered in sores. 'Tell me Hanneli, where am I?' Anne asked. 'Is it Auschwitz?'

'No, my dear. They have moved you to another camp.'

A look of pain came into Anne's eyes.

'But Mummy and Daddy are at Auschwitz. I want to see them.' She made a sobbing sound, but no tears came.

Hanneli grasped her hand. 'Don't cry, Anne. It will soon be over and then you will be with them again.'

Anne slowly closed her eyes. 'Soon be over? Yes, thank God, it will soon be over.'

Hanneli stayed with Anne until she was sure that she was asleep. Then, kissing her friend lightly on the forehead, she went out into the night.

The Frank family was taken first to Westerbork camp, then to the Auschwitz concentration camp. Here the men and women were separated. At the end of October 1944 Anne and Margot, both seriously ill, were moved to Belsen concentration camp. Margot died sometime in March, Anne just a few days later. British troops reached Belsen on 15 April 1945.

The Victims

Edith Frank, Anne's mother, died in Auschwitz on 6 January 1945. Mr and Mrs van Pels, Peter and Mr Pfeffer also died at the hands of the Nazis. Otto Frank, Anne's father, was the only one from the secret flat to survive. The Russians rescued him from Auschwitz on 27 January 1945. It took him seven months to find out what had happened to Margot and Anne.

We do not know exactly how many Jews the Nazis killed during the war. It was probably about six million, the greatest slaughter in human history.

Anne Frank's Diary

After the Franks had been taken prisoner, Miep Gies went to the secret flat and found Anne's diary. She kept it, hoping to give it back after the war. When she learned that Anne was dead, she gave it to Otto Frank. In 1947, he arranged for it to be published in Dutch. Since then it has been translated into more than 50 languages and read by millions of people. Thanks to Anne's young talent, her memory and that of all the other victims of Nazi racism will live for ever.

Timeline

1929	12 June	Anne Frank is born in Frankfurt, Germany.
1933		Frank family moves to Amsterdam, Holland, to escape from the Nazis.
1934		Anne starts school.
1940	May	The Nazis invade Holland.
1941		Margot and Anne move to the Jewish secondary school, Amsterdam.
1942	12 June	Anne receives Kitty, her diary, for her thirteenth birthday.
1942	6 July	The Frank family goes into hiding.
1944	4 August	Nazis discover the secret flat and arrest everyone there.
	3 Sept	The eight Jews from the secret flat are sent to Auschwitz concentration camp, Poland.
	October	Margot and Anne are moved to Belsen concentration camp, Germany.
1945	6 January	Edith Frank dies.
	27 January	The Russians free Otto Frank from Auschwitz.
	March	Margot and Anne die.
1947		Anne's diary is published in Dutch.
1980		Otto Frank dies, aged 91.

More Information

Books to read

The Diary of a Young Girl by
Anne Frank, Penguin 1997.
Anne Frank by John Rowley,
Heinemann 1999.
Anne Frank by Harriet Castor,
Watts 1996.
Anne Frank by Rachel Epstein,
Watts 1997.
The Last Days of Freedom by Roy
Apps, Macdonald Young Books 1998.

Websites

http://www.annefrank.nl
http://www.annefrank.com

Museum

Otto Frank's workplace at
263 Prinsengracht in Amsterdam is
now a museum called Anne Frank
House. Visitors can see the secret flat
and many other objects that belonged
to the eight people who hid there.

Glossary

Auschwitz The largest Nazi
concentration camp, in Poland. The
Nazis killed one and a half million
people at Auschwitz, many with gas.

Belsen Also known as Bergen-
Belsen, this was a huge concentration
camp in northern Germany.

book-keeping Writing down all the
money a business takes in and pays out.

concentration camp A large prison
made up of huts surrounded by high
fences of barbed wire.

Nazi The Nazis ruled Germany
from 1933 to 1945. Their leader
was Adolf Hitler. He believed that
all Jews were evil. Hitler's supporters
organized the deaths of about
six million Jews.

Star of David The six-pointed
star that is the symbol of the Jewish
people. The Nazis made all Jews
wear a Star of David so they
could be recognized.

work camp The Nazi name
for a concentration camp.

Index